# The Disgusted Dragon

by Kay Brophy

with illustrations by Katy Boys

First published in the UK in 2017 by Middle Farm Press
British Library Cataloguing-in-Publication Data
A catalogue record for this book is available from the British Library
ISBN 978-0-9928896-7-8

Published by Middle Farm Press
Author: Kay Brophy
Managing Editor: Kate Taylor
Illustrator: Katy Boys
Designer: Su Richards
Printed by Think Digital Books Ltd

To my husband, Pete

# Lifeland

STATION OF
SURPRISE

ANGER ARCHES

SAD STONES

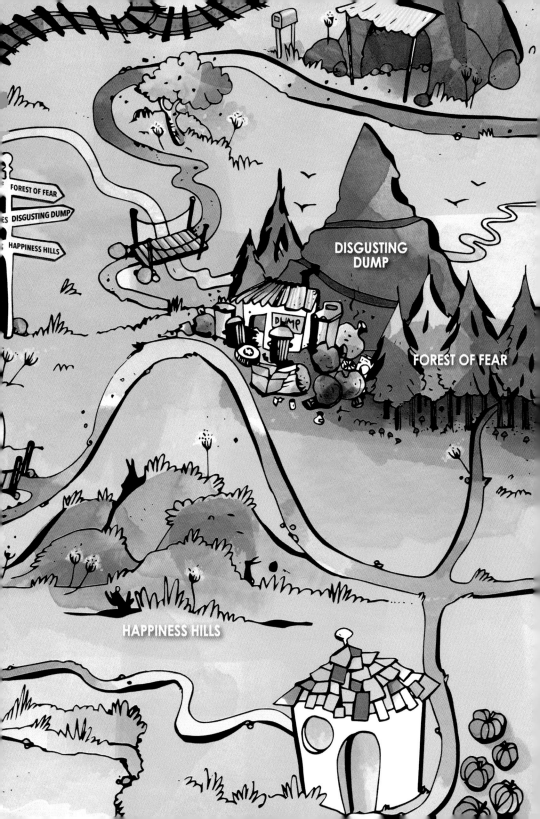

There once lived a dragon,
    so strong and so mighty
He lived in a den that was spotless and tidy
Outside stood a dump where rubbish was thrown
Dirty and smelly,
    a bit overgrown

He never went out, or had people to stay
He assumed that nobody would want
to come play

Day after day, he stayed underground
Not making a mess, not making a sound

But the dump was actually a brilliant place
For exploring, for playing, for having a race
The junk could be used to dress up or play games
To slide down a hill or to shout out friends' names

The dragon was lonely,
and never had fun
He couldn't even remember how it was done
But one day a knight appeared,
as it started to snow
She looked brave and gallant,
a proper hero

The knight
was called Nu
and she loved
having fun

Her clothes where so scruffy, her laces undone

She had great big blue eyes and
messy blonde hair
She may have looked tatty
but she didn't care

'I know that you're in there,
please come out and play'
'I'm a knight and I need a fierce dragon to slay'

'This place is amazing,
there's treasure all round'
'Just wait till you see all the things
that I've found'

'I've made a shield and a sword,
and something for you'
'Oh please come out, it's more
fun with two!'

The Dragon decided to open his door
He was interested now and keen to know more
'You've made something for me?
And you just want to play?'
'But I'll surely get filthy,
it won't wash away'

'Yes it will, just use water
       and plenty of bubbles'
'If you don't have a bath you can
       always use puddles!'
'Getting dirty is great,
       it's all part of the fun'
'It washes away
       when your playing is done'

The dragon stepped out and looked all around
He felt nervous and almost
                went back underground
'Come on' said Nu kindly and held out her hand
'Let me show you around this fabulous land'

Old shoes and tyres,
saucepans and spoons
All came to life, and some even made tunes!
She could turn junk to treasure by using her mind
If he used his imagination, what might he find?

pirate's telescope

Saucepan helmet

flip flop tennis

They played every day
    and their friendship just grew
No longer disgusted, he saw things anew
The dragon learned something important that day
He realised that 'big' feelings
    CAN go away

Sometimes we see
things through negative eyes
But we find our way by being clever and wise
A friend with big ideas had helped
Dragon get through
And if you feel disgusted you can change
your thoughts too